Level 4

Duet Favorites

by Jane Smisor Bastien

Contents

kjos Neil A. Kjos Music Company • Publisher

The Entertainer

Secondo

Scott Joplin

The Entertainer

Primo

Scott Joplin

4

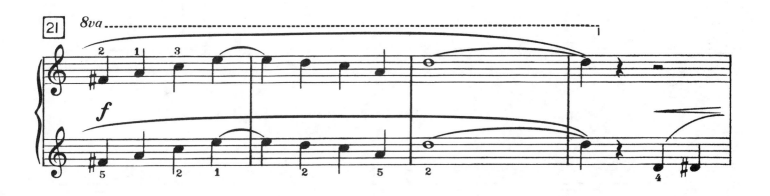

WP63

6

Boogie Woogie Bill

Secondo

Boogie Woogie Bill

Primo

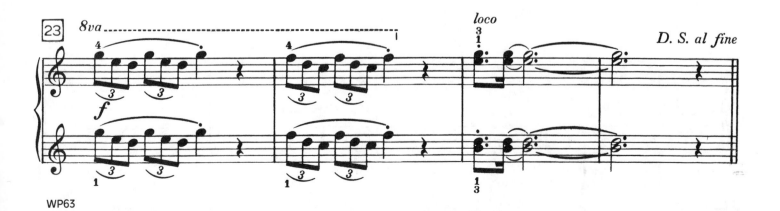

WP63

Rondo Fantastique

Secondo

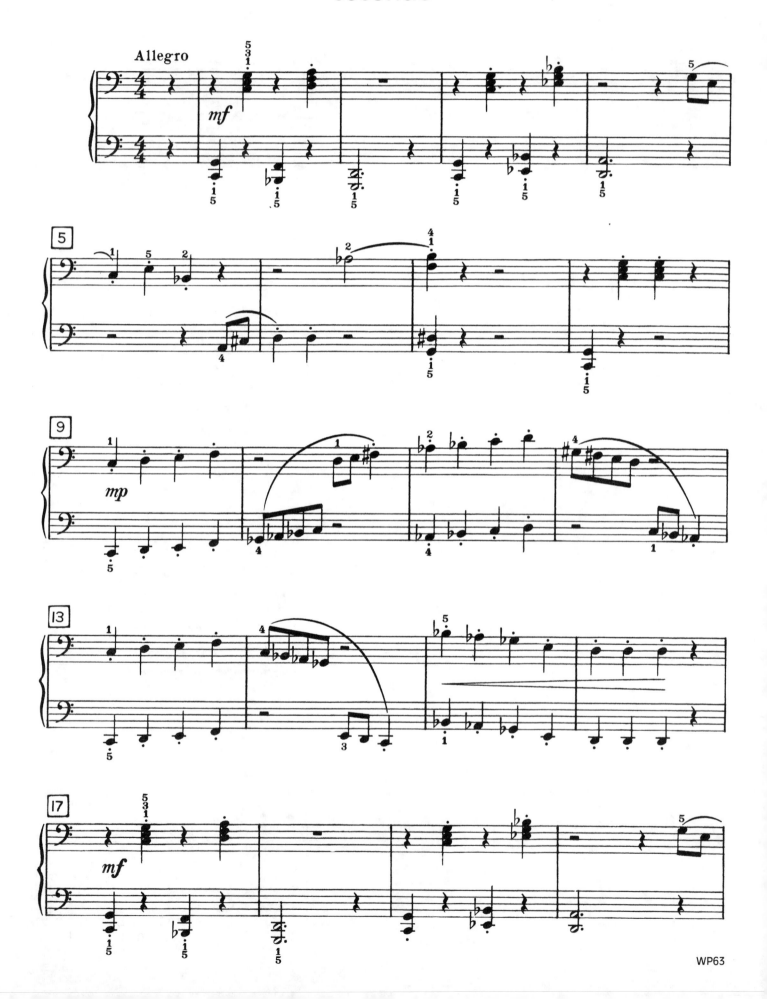

Rondo Fantastique
Primo

WP63

Turkey in the Straw

Secondo

Folk Song

Turkey in the Straw

Primo

Folk Song

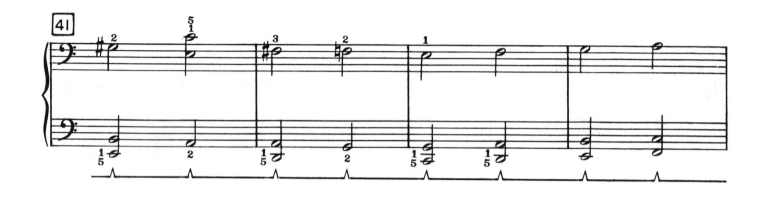

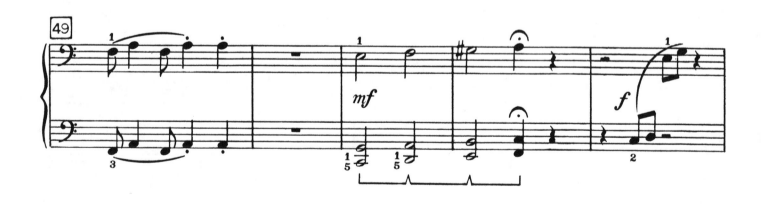

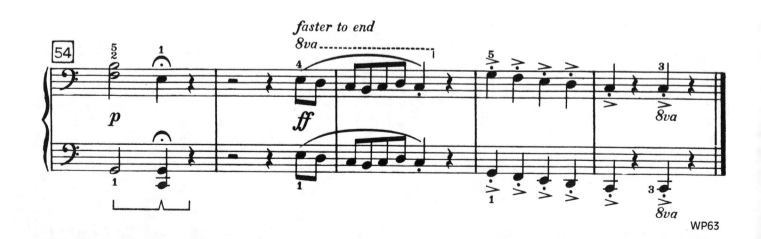

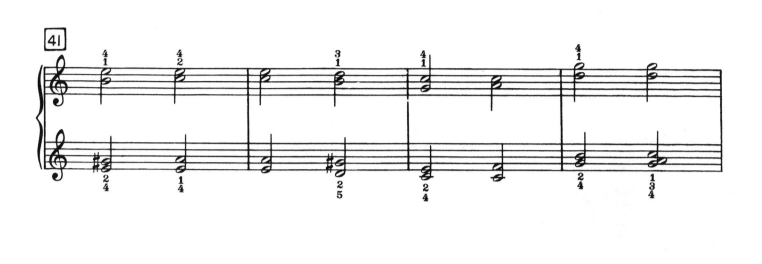

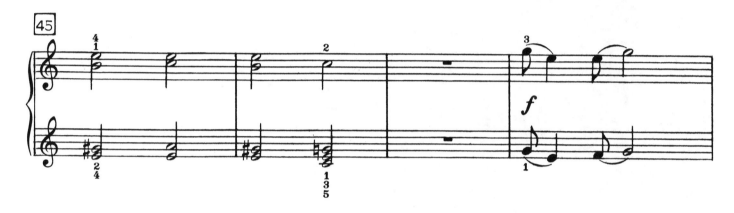

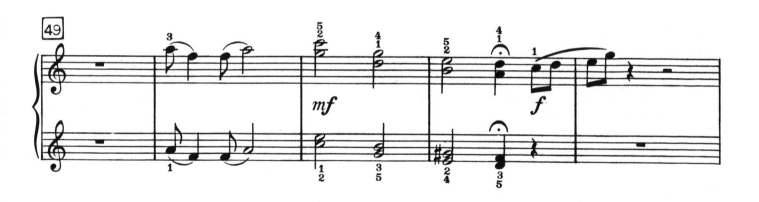

faster to end

8va -

WP63

POP PIANO STYLES

A light and refreshing collection of rock, blues, boogie, and disco styles from Jane and James Bastien. From foot-stompin' rhythms to melancholy moods, these up-to-date sounds encourage practicing and performing for pianists of all ages!

Levels 1-4

Level 1
WP51

Level 2
WP52

Level 3
WP53

Level 4
WP54